SIT. STAY.

forever.

Angela Hunt

illustrated by
Mursalier Asker

Published 2020, by Hunt Haven Press

Hunt Haven

For Patton, Ike, Sadie, Justus,
Dani, Billy, Babe, Charley, Ivy
and Jazzy.

We're going to need a big yard in heaven.

*W*hen the woman placed the eager
puppy in my arms,
those dancing eyes said

I like you. Let's play.

When I took the puppy to my vet and she saw the stranger with the needles, those big brown eyes said

I want YOU. Let's play.

$\mathcal{W}$hen we went to obedience school and I barked out orders and tugged on the leash, her wide brown eyes said

I'll do it if we can play.

*W*hen she got sick and I hid her pill beneath a generous dollop of gravy, she licked up the gravy and left the pill in her bowl. When she looked at me, her eyes said

Ha! Can't fool me. Let's play.

*A*s time passed and her gait
slowed and her muzzle grayed,
she would put her head in my lap.
Her gaze would meet mine
and her eyes said

I love you no matter what.
We don't have to play.

*O*ne day she limped over to me,
sat as I'd taught her,
and patiently waited for me to
decipher the message in her eyes.
I could read it in her heavy panting
and the weary slope of her shoulders.
As much as I wanted to ignore
her meaning, I couldn't.

I trust you. Make the hurt go away.

$\mathcal{B}$ecause God created man to be
a benevolent steward of all creatures
great and small,
and because I loved my dog,
I drew a deep breath and
called the vet.

As my beautiful beast lay in her bed,
I cradled her head, weeping,
and promised I'd meet her in that place
where all things are made new and eternal.

I'll be there, she said,
closing her eyes.
And we'll play.

Then I saw a new heaven and a new earth;
for the first heaven and
the first earth had passed away . . .
Revelation 21:1

In that day the wolf and the lamb will live together;
the leopard will lie down with the baby goat.
The calf and the yearling will be safe with the lion,
and a little child will lead them all.
. . .
Nothing will hurt or destroy in all my holy mountain,
for as the waters fill the sea,
so the earth will be filled with people
who know the Lord.
--Isaiah 11:6, 9

You may paste a picture of your
beloved dog into this frame.

You are welcome to visit our
Sit Stay Forever Facebook
page and post a photo of your
dog. Be sure to tell us
about your beloved pet.
We will understand.

Sit Stay Forever on Facebook.

CPSIA information can be obtained
at www.ICGtesting.com
Printed in the USA
LVHW102226171120
671253LV00053B/733/J

9 781735 604008